Animal Friends

Faces

FOG CITY PRESS

Your face can
say a lot.

Your face can say you
are feeling happy.

Your face can say you
are very excited.

Your face can say you want
to know what is going on.

There can be times when you want to hide your face.

Did you do something bad?

Were you rude?

Did you get angry?

Were you caught by surprise?

Did you see something funny?

Or are you feeling sad?

Open your eyes wide.

The world is full
of things that can
make you smile.

So, put on a brave face.

Try to stay cool.

Maybe take a little break.

But don't stop being curious.

Keep exploring.

Let yourself be silly.

Laugh out loud.

Look at the world
in another way.

Always look for the things that put a smile on your face.

Introducing...Your Animal Friends!

 Nosy ostrich

 Curious dog

 Rude dog

 Smiling frog

 Nosy donkey

 Angry camel

 Laughing horse

 Hiding orangutan

 Upset horse

 Grinning donkey

 Bad monkey

 Surprised monkey

 Excited cat

 Guilty raccoons

 Chuckling pig

 Happy dog

 Cheeky giraffe

 Laughing zebra

Quiet koala

 Cool sheep

 Silly cow

 Sad marmoset

 Calm gibbon

 Laughing monkey

 Wide-eyed frog

 Sleepy kitten

 Amused fox

 Alert cat

 Peering ostrich

 Funny orangutan

 Laughing owl

 Curious cat

 Smiling dolphin

 Brave dog

 Peeking squirrel

 Cool orangutan

 Patient meerkat

 Daring kitten

Published by Fog City Press,
a division of Weldon Owen Inc.
415 Jackson Street
San Francisco, CA 94111
www.weldonowen.com

WELDON OWEN GROUP
Chief Executive Officer John Owen

WELDON OWEN INC.
President, Chief Executive Officer Terry Newell
Vice President, International Sales Stuart Laurence
Vice President, Sales and New Business Development Amy Kan
Vice President, Sales—Asia and Latin America Dawn Low
Vice President, Publisher Roger Shaw
Vice President, Creative Director Gaye Allen
Managing Editor, Fog City Press Karen Perez
Assistant Editor Sonia Vallabh
Art Directors Bret Hansen and Heather Stewart
Designer Andreas Schueller
Design Assistant Kevin Yuen
Production Director Chris Hemesath
Production Manager Michelle Duggan
Color Manager Teri Bell

Text Karen Perez & Sonia Vallabh
Picture Research Brandi Valenza

A WELDON OWEN PRODUCTION

Library of Congress Control Number: 2008926983

ISBN-13: 978-1-74089-757-0

10 9 8 7 6 5 4 3 2 1

Color separations by San Choy International, Singapore.
Printed by Tien Wah Press in Singapore.

Image Credits: Key iSP=iStockphoto; SST=Shutterstock
Front cover SST; 1 iSP; 2 SST; 4 SST; 5 iSP; 6 SST; 7 SST; 8 SST; 9 iS
10 SST; 12 iSP; 13 SST; 14 iSP; 15 SST; 16 SST; 17 SST; 18 SST; 20 SST;
21 SST; 22 SST; 23 SST; 24 iSP; 25 SST; 26 SST; 28 iSP; 29 SST; 30 i
31 SST; 33 SST; 34 SST; 36 iSP; 37 iSP; 38 SST; 39 SST; 40 SST; 41 iS
42 SST; 45 SST; 48 SST.